This
Dora the Explorer Annual
belongs to

Contents

EGMONT
We bring stories to life

First published in Great Britain 2011 by Egmont UK Limited, 239 Kensington High Street, London W8 6SA
Activities and story adaptations by Laura Milne.

© 2011 Viacom International Inc. All rights reserved.
Nickelodeon, Nick Jr., Dora the Explorer and all related titles, logos and characters are trademarks of Viacom International Inc.

ISBN 978 1 4052 5815 9
1 3 5 7 9 10 8 6 4 2
Printed in Italy

Adult supervision recommended when sharp implements, such as scissors, are in use.

At Home

Dora lives with her family in a yellow house, **casa**. She lives with her mummy, **mami**, daddy, **papi** and her twin brother and sister.

How many windows can you see?

Write your answer here:

8

Use this space to draw
your own family.

What
colour is
your
house?

How
many purple
flowers can
you see?

Write your
answer
here:

9

Dora's Friends

How well do you know Dora's friends? Read each line and decide whether the answer is yes, sí, or no, no. Draw a circle around each answer.

Backpack always stays at home.

yes, sí   no, no

Boots is a monkey.

yes, sí   no, no

Map shows Dora which way to go.

yes, sí   no, no

Colour Boots' boots bright red!

Isa is green – give her some colour!

Benny is a cat.
yes, **sí** no, **no**

Isa loves growing flowers.
yes, **sí** no, **no**

Tico drives a yellow car.
yes, **sí** no, **no**

Swiper tries to swipe things.
yes, **sí** no, **no**

Colourful Dora

Colour in Dora, using the small picture as a guide.

Now shout 'Hello, ¡Hola!' out loud.

Sport Fun

Dora and Boots love playing sport. Draw circles around the items they can play with.

What sports do you like playing?

13

Wonderful Wildlife Park

Dora and Boots are in a wildlife park. Help them find the way out. Make sure they pass all the animals on their way!

Start

Finish

How many animals did Dora and Boots see?

Write your answer here:

14

Farmyard Counting

Here is Benny's barn. Count how many pigs, sheep and cows are in the picture. Then trace over the numbers.

2

3

1

Where is Benny? Point to him!

Dora's Jack-in-the-Box

¡Hola! Boots and I are going to the toy shop. My twin baby brother and sister have been poorly. I want to buy them a toy. Come inside with us!

What are your favourite toys?

The Jack-in-the-box is calling us!
He wants us to take him home.
Let's see what happens if I turn the handle.
Whilst I do that, join me and sing 'Pop!
Goes the Weasel'.

Half a pound of tuppenny rice,
Half a pound of treacle,
Mix it up and make it nice,
Pop! Goes the Weasel!

Look, when we sang 'Pop!',
Jack popped out of his box.
My brother and sister would
love Jack. We'll take him
home. Let's go! ¡Vámonos!

17

Let's ask Map how to get to my house.

Map says we need to go past the Russian doll and then through the Piano Gate. Listen, what's that rustling sound?

Oh no, it's Swiper! He'll swipe our Jack-in-the-box. Say 'Swiper, no swiping' three times to stop him.

We stopped Swiper. Excellent! ¡Excelente!

We've found the Russian doll, but she is blocking the path. She cannot find her dolls because they are so little, **pequeños**.

Do you see the little dolls? How many are there?

Write your answer here:

Four. **Cuatro**. Well done! **¡Muy bien!** We've helped the Russian doll find her little dolls. Now she will let us past.

It's a long way to the Piano Gate.
Do you see someone who can
give us a lift?

Look, here's Tico in his car.
He can give us a lift.

Oh no! There are
potholes in the road.
We need to tell Tico to
look out for the next hole,
hoyo and to be careful,
cuidado. Tico only speaks
Spanish, so say after me
'¡Un hoyo, cuidado!'

We've now safely arrived at
the Piano Gate. Thanks, Tico
¡Gracias, Tico!

The Piano Gate wants us to sing along with the tune she's playing. Let's sing together!

Row, row, row your boat gently down the stream, Merrily, merrily, merrily, merrily, life is but a dream.

A barco is something you use in the water to float. Can you guess what it is?

That's right, it's a boat!

Now we're able to walk through the Piano Gate. Let's go! ¡Vámonos!

Okay, we're almost there. Let's take Jack-in-the-box to my house! Oh no! Jack has tumbled and fallen out of his box and the box fell into the bushes.

How many bushes can you see?

That's right. Five, **cinco**. Let's help Jack find his box.

What colour is this?
Blue, azul.

And this colour?
Red, rojo.

And what colour is this?
Green, verde.

What is this colour?
Yellow, amarillo.

Now, what's the last colour?
Orange, naranja.

Well done, we did it! We found Jack's box in the yellow, **amarillo** bush and he's happy again now.

Great, we've made it back to my house!
Look, here are the twins. ¡Hola Guillermo! ¡Hola Isabella!
They are feeling better now and they
love their new toy.

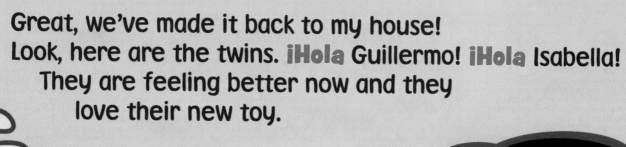

Which baby
do you think
is Guillermo?
Which is
Isabella?

We did it! Lo hicimos!
Thanks for helping us
bring Jack home. We
couldn't have done it
without you.

It's Playtime!

Look at all these toys!
Draw a line to match the pairs.

Draw your favourite toy here.

B is for ...

Boots' name begins with the letter 'b'. Trace over the letters to write other words that begin with 'b'.

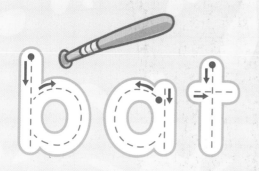

bat

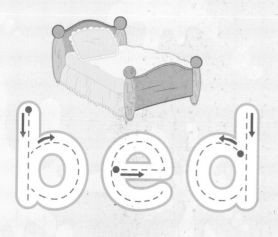

bed

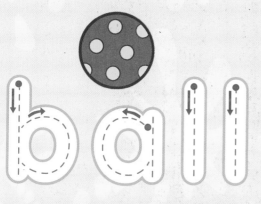

ball

Boots' favourite food begins with 'b'. What is it? Shout the name out loud!

Dot-to-dot

Who is jumping with Dora and Boots?
Join the dots to find out!

Now colour in the rest of the picture.

26

Odd One Out

These four pictures of Dora and Boots look the same but one is different. Which is the odd one out?

a

b

c

d

How many snowflakes are on this page?

Write your answer here:

Isa's Unicorn Flowers

¡**Hola!** Isa and I are planting flowers. Do you want to help us? Great! To get the flowers to grow, we have to say, '**¡Crezcan, flores!**'. Grow, flowers!

Well done! **¡Muy bien!** The flowers have grown. How many number flowers are there? Right, there are five, **cinco**.

There are also some special flowers shaped like a cone. They are Isa's special unicorn flowers.

Where are the butterfly flowers?

Look, there is a rainbow near the unicorn flowers. Let's explore and see what is at the end of the rainbow.

There is a unicorn at the end of the rainbow!
His name is Unicornio. The unicorn flowers are
his mummy's favourite. We can give Unicornio
some flowers to take home.

Unicornio rode here
on the rainbow. But
the rainbow is fading!
Do you want to join us
to help find it again?

How many
unicorn
flowers are
there?

Write your
answer
here:

Excellent! ¡Excelente!
We will take Unicornio
home to the other
end of the rainbow.

Let's ask Map how to get to the other end of the rainbow.

Map says we need to go past the Dragon's Cave and over the Troll Bridge.

We're at the Cave, but the Dragon is blocking our way. Look, there's my friend Mei. She is from China and she knows some dragon stories. Maybe she can help.

31

Mei says that if we all do the Dragon Dance, the Dragon will move out of the way.

Stomp your feet. Stomp, stomp, stomp!
Flap your arms. Flap, flap, flap!
And roar. Roar!

Great, our dance worked. The Dragon has danced into the cave. ¡Gracias, Mei! Let's go to the Troll Bridge.

We have found the Troll Bridge. But the Grumpy Old Troll says we need to solve this riddle before we can cross the bridge.

He looks like a pony. On his head is a horn. Which is he? Tick the right one.

That's right! It's the unicorn! Now we can cross the Troll Bridge and look for the rainbow. Let's go! ¡Vámonos!

We need to climb to the top of the beanstalk to reach the rainbow.

Some of the leaves are too small for Unicornio to climb onto. You can help by pointing to the biggest leaves.

Which is the biggest leaf of all?

¡Gracias! Thank you! Now we can climb to the top of the beanstalk.

Wheeeeeee!

Boots and I are riding Unicornio down the rainbow.

Point to the waterfall.

We did it! We've brought Unicornio home to the forest. He can now give the flowers to his mummy. Thanks for helping. ¡Gracias!

Isa's Garden

Dora's helping Isa
plant pretty flowers.
Finish colouring in
the picture.

How many
bees can
you see?

Write your
answer
here:

Seaside Spot the Difference

Dora and Boots are exploring the seaside. These two pictures look the same, but there are 5 differences in picture 2.

Colour in an ice cream for each difference you find.

Benny's Treasure

Find out what happens on junk day! When you see a picture, say the name out loud.

Benny   Backpack   Map   Boots

Swiper   Grumpy Old Troll   Yuki

It's junk day, and we are putting some old things out

for the junk truck to pick up.  thinks lots

of the junk is treasure.

He puts some of the treasure in his wagon.

Oh no! The junk truck has taken  and

away by mistake.  ,  and I will rescue

them from the junkyard! We need to go over the Troll

Bridge, then across Swan Lake. Uh-oh, I hear  .

He'll try to swipe our wagon! To stop him, say 'Swiper, no

swiping!' three times. We did it, we stopped !

At the Troll Bridge, the  won't let us cross.

We need to make some music for him, using the treasure

from the wagon. We ring an alarm clock and honk a horn.

Great, the  lets us cross his bridge!

Now on to Swan Lake. My friend  helps us

cross the lake. She makes a big swan out of paper. We fly

over the lake, riding the swan! Now we have arrived at the

junkyard. There is  and  !

We have rescued them. Thanks for helping! ¡Gracias!

Colour in the picture.

Swan Origami

Dora, Benny and Boots flew across the lake on a swan made out of paper! Follow these steps to make your own paper swan.

Ask an adult to help you with this!

You will need:

A square piece of paper, measuring about 200 x 200 mm. You can use proper origami paper, or plain paper.

1

Fold the paper along one diagonal, then unfold it.

Swans are normally white, but you can use any colour paper you like!

42

3

Turn the paper over. Make a double fold on one side, bringing the outer edge into the centre.

2

Now fold the lower edges of the square into the centre line.

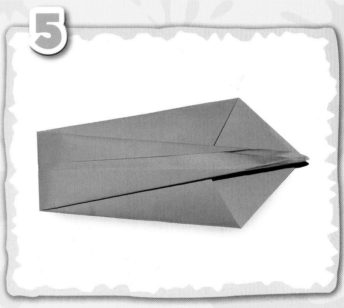

5

Now fold the pointed end of the paper upwards, about halfway. The swan is starting to take shape now!

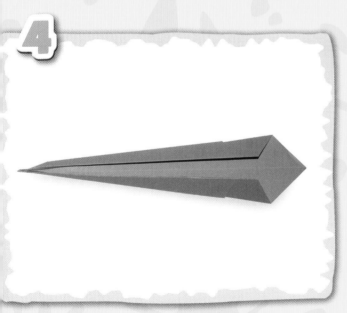

4

Make a double fold on the other side.

6

Next, fold the top of the pointed section down towards the middle. This is the swan's head.

7

Pull the neck of the swan away from the body. The swan is now finished!

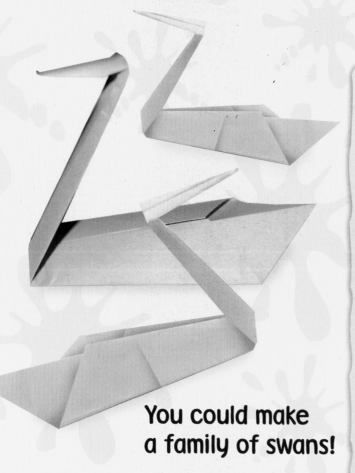

You could make a family of swans!

Swans can fly!

Circle the other creatures that can fly.

Back to School

Dora is getting ready for school. Tick the 4 things that she should take.

Which of the objects can be eaten? Draw it here.

First Day of School

Let's go to school!

¡Hola! Today is the first day of school for Boots and Tico. They are going to the same school as me. Are you going to come with us? Great!

Let's ask Map how to get to the school.

Map says we need to cross the River and go through the Forest to get to school. We can learn some words on our way to the River.

Look there are some birds Hello, birds! ¡Hola, pájaros! And there's a frog. Hello, frog! ¡Hola, rana!

How many birds can you see?

Write your answer here:

We've made it to the River! There is a big turtle, **tortuga**. He is hiding in the bushes with his friends.

How many turtles can you see?

Write your answer here:

One, **uno**.
Two, **dos**.
Three, **tres**.
That's right, there are three turtles, **tres tortugas**.

Now we have to cross the River. We need to ride the turtles to get across. We need to find the turtle that is the right size for each of us. Can you help?

Draw lines to match Dora and her friends to the correct turtle. Dora needs to ride the biggest turtle, Boots the second biggest and Tico the smallest turtle.

Now point to the biggest turtle!

We did it! We crossed the River by riding on the turtles. Now we can go to the Forest.

Uh-oh, that sounds like Swiper the fox. He is swiping Boots' and Tico's lunchboxes!

When you see Swiper, point to him.

Bananas, plátanos!

Nuts, nueces!

What colour are the bananas?

Boots' lunchbox had bananas inside it. Tico's lunchbox had walnuts inside it. Swiper has thrown them into the tree. Can you see the bananas and walnuts?

To help get the bananas down from the tree, we need to shout, bananas, plátanos! To get the walnuts down from the tree, we need to shout, nuts, nueces!

51

Great, we did it! We've got the bananas and walnuts back.

We've crossed the River and gone through the Forest. Now, where do we go next? Tick the box.

That's right. Number 3, the school. La escuela!

We did it! We followed the path after the Forest and we've arrived at the school. Now Boots and Tico can start their very first day there.

The Night Sky

Papi, Boots and I are exploring the sky at night!

Oh no! Swiper wants to swipe our telescope!

If you see Swiper, say 'Swiper, no swiping!' three times. Then colour him in.

Tick here if you've ever seen the real moon!

Tick a box when you find each object!

55

Boots' Banana Wish

¡Hola! Boots and I are at a fairground. There is a wishing machine. Can you guess what Boots will wish for?

Right, bananas. Each time Boots says 'bananas', he gets bananas! But now there are too many bananas. Boots isn't happy, as they are landing on his head.

How many butterflies can you see?

Write your answer here:

Boots wants to wish for no more bananas, but the wishing machine has broken. We need to find another one. Roberto the Robot's grandfather has a wishing machine in his workshop.

Let's ask Map the quickest way to the workshop.

Map says we need to go over the Troll Bridge, then across the Big River. Let's go! ¡Vámonos!

Here we are at the Troll Bridge. The Grumpy Old Troll will only let us cross the bridge if we solve his riddle.

What grows in a bunch under the sun, And is yellow and yummy – can you guess this one?

It's a banana. Well done! ¡Muy bien! Now we can go over the bridge.

Some turtles are blocking the path. We need to let them know that we are coming through. In English, we say, 'Watch out, turtles'. In Spanish, we say, 'Cuidado, tortugas'.

Thank you! ¡Gracias! Now we can carry on to the Big River.

Find all 8 turtles.

We've made it to the Big River! The Pirate Piggies are there, with their boat. They can give us a lift across the river.

The boat uses bananas for fuel, but the Piggies have run out of bananas. Boots can help. What do you think Boots needs to say?

Bananas!

Right, bananas! Now we can sail across the river. Thanks, Piggies! ¡Gracias!

Oo oo, ah ah!

Oo oo, ah ah!

There is the workshop.
But the path is really slippery.
It is covered in banana skins!
We can swing on the tree vines
to get over the banana skins.

You can try this with us. Reach up
to grab the tree vines. Put your arms
above your head and reach, reach, reach!
Now say 'Oo oo, ah ah!'.

We did it!
Lo
hicimos!

We've made it to Roberto's grandfather's workshop!
Boots can now make his new wish on the wishing machine.
He wishes that bananas would stop falling on him every
time he says 'bananas'!

Great, it worked.
Bananas are no
longer falling on
Boots. Thanks for
helping, everybody!
¡Gracias!

Time for a Wish

Boots wished for lots of bananas in that story!
What would you like to wish for? Draw it here.

How many stars are on this page?

Write your answer here:

Shadow Match

Dora has lots of friends, amigos! Draw lines to match each picture to its shadow.

What are your friends called? Call out their names!

a

b

c

d

1

2

3

4

Dora's Word List

English	Spanish	Say
bananas	plátanos	PLAH-tah-nohs
birds	pájaros	PAH-hah-rohs
blue	azul	ah-SOOL
boat	barco	BAR-coh
careful	cuidado	kwee-DAH-doh
daddy	papi	PAH-pee
excellent	excelente	ex-seh-LEN-tay
fantastic	fantástico	fahn-TAHS-tee-koh
five	cinco	SIN-koh
flowers	flores	FLOHR-ehz
four	cuatro	QWAH-troh
friends	amigos	ah-MEE-gohs
frog	rana	RAH-nah
green	verde	VEHR-day
hello	hola	OH-lah

English	Spanish	Say
hole	hoyo	OY-yoh
house	casa	CAH-sa
let's go	vámonos	VAH-moh-nohs
little	pequeño	peh-KEHN-yoh
mummy	mami	MAH-mee
no	no	noh
nuts	nueces	noo-EH-sehz
one	uno	OO-noh
orange	naranja	nah-RAHN-hah
red	rojo	ROH-hoh
school	escuela	ess-KWAY-lah
thanks	gracias	GRAH-see-ahs
three	tres	trehs
two	dos	dohs
we did it	lo hicimos	loh-ee-SEE-mohs
well done	muy bien	MUH-byen
yellow	amarillo	ah-mah-REE-yoh
yes	sí	see

Answers

Ladybird Hunt
Page 7 - there are ladybirds on pages 10, 17, 21, 25, 33, 46, 50, 53, 56 and 60.

At Home
Page 8 - 5 windows.
Page 9 - 10 purple flowers.

Dora's Friends
Page 10 - yes, Boots is a monkey.
No, Backpack goes everywhere with Dora.
Yes, Map shows Dora which way to go.
Yes, Isa loves growing flowers.
No, Benny is a bull.
Yes, Tico drives a yellow car.
Yes, Swiper tries to swipe things.

Sport Fun
Page 13

Wonderful Wildlife Park
Page 14 - 6 animals.

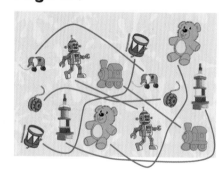

Dora's Jack-in-the-Box
Page 19 - 4 little dolls.

It's Playtime!
Page 24

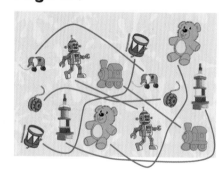

Dot-to-dot
Page 26 - it's Benny!

Odd One Out
Page 27 - c is the odd one out as the hat is green.
Page 27 - 8 snowflakes.

Isa's Unicorn Flowers
Page 30 - 7 unicorn flowers.
Page 33 - unicorn.

Isa's Garden
Page 36 - 6 bees.

Seaside Spot the Differen
Page 37

Swan Origami
Page 44 - the owl and ba can fly.

Back to School
Page 45 - Dora should ta the pencil, book, apple an paintbrush.
The apple can be eaten.

First Day of School
Page 47 - 4 birds.
Page 48 - 3 turtles.

Boots' Banana Wish
Page 57 - 7 bananas.
Page 58 - 5 butterflies.
Page 59 - banana.

Time for a Wish
Page 64 - 11 stars (including the one on the wishing machine).

Shadow Match
Page 65
a - 4, b - 3, c - 1, d - 2